Angels All Around Us

By Christopher Paul Carter

Illustrated by Skye Como Miller

Graphic Design by Erica Littauer

THE FIG & THE VINE
PUBLISHING, LLC

Dedication

For every reader, young at heart,
who has always known
that there is more to this world
than what you can see with your eyes.

I hope this book confirms your wildest notions
that angels are, indeed, all around us!

Requests for permission to make copies of any part of this work should be emailed to (subject: Permissions) figandvine@mail.com.

Library of Congress Cataloging-in-Publication Data
Carter, Christopher Paul
Angels All Around Us / by Christopher Paul Carter;
illustrated by Skye Como Miller—1st ed.
p. cm.
Summary: Angels are all around us and can appear in many different ways.
ISBN 978-0-578-60456-5
[1. Religious / Christian / Early Readers. 2. Religious / Christian / Inspirational. 3. Paranormal & Supernatural.]

Manufactured in the United States of America

10 9 8 7 6 5 4 3 2 1

For the Reader

As you open this book, you'll need two things: your sense of wonder and your imagination. You're about to open a book about angels! As soon as you start reading (or reading it to someone you love), you will begin to imagine a spiritual world, and you'll start to see how the world of the angels is connected to the world we live in.

There are two ways to see angels. First, God can "open the eyes of your heart" to see angels and other heavenly things as easily as you see the things around you right now. That's happened to people before, and the Bible is full of those stories. The other way is to see how the heavenly angels are connected to the things you see every day on this earth. Did you know that the Bible talks about angels being like wind, fire, and stars? Well, those are things you see all the time! Maybe it's easier to see angels than we've ever imagined. Maybe they're all around us and connected to us through all the beautiful parts of this world that God has made!

When we created this book, we hoped it would help you imagine your world – and the angels – in a whole new way. We thought the illustrations might help you do that, but these are just our ideas of what angels can look like and how some of them looked to us. The Bible paints a picture for us of many different kinds of spiritual beings. Some look more human-like and have names like Gabriel, and some are described as fiery winged creatures called seraphim. We've illustrated the angels in this book in different ways, too. Some look like people with wings, and some look like a part of nature that you see every day. It's a lot of fun to imagine what angels could look like!

At the end of the book, you can imagine and even draw your own angel! And we've provided some notes on how each angel here is connected to a scripture verse or historical figure, and how we chose the illustrations to spark our imaginations.

Are you ready to have a fun journey with God's awesome angels?

Did you ever wonder where the angels are?
And what do they do all day?

Did you know that some are sent to protect us?
But maybe others just like to play.

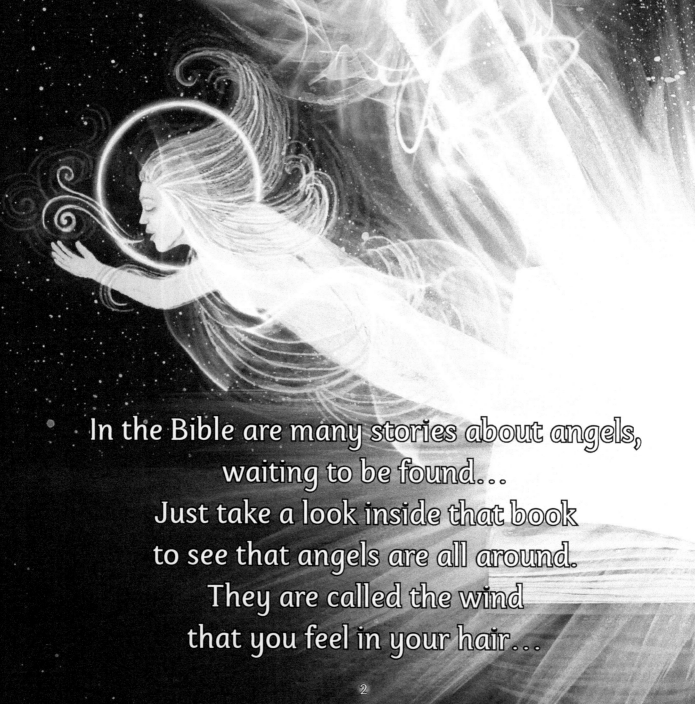

In the Bible are many stories about angels,
waiting to be found...
Just take a look inside that book
to see that angels are all around.
They are called the wind
that you feel in your hair...

Flames of fire
that keep you warm on a cold night...
The stars in the heavens soaring high up above
and coloring the sky with their light.

The Bible calls them Virtues,
which means you'll know they are near
when you feel

Peace,

Patience,

or Courage…

When you know not to fear!

They are sent to help us, take care of us,
and they are with us everyday.

Some people even talked with them,
or saw them when they prayed.

A man named John saw an angel standing in the sun.
Another one held an important key.
Still another was sent to protect a child.
I wonder if any of these angels are close to me?

Perhaps it's the angel standing in the river,
Gabriel was his name.

Or maybe it's the one at the gate to the Garden,
guarding the way with his flame.

A man named St. Patrick, who lived long ago,
met an angel named Victor
whom he really got to know!

Patrick said he met with Victor
just like you meet with your friend.

God, is there an angel who watches over me?
Is there an angel you can send?

I wonder if one has a halo, like the planet Saturn…
Or maybe one reflects the silvery light of the moon…

I wonder if one shook the earth with his joy
when Jesus came out of the tomb?!

8

Angels were there to tell the disciples
that Jesus made everything new...

And they watched as Jesus went back to Heaven
to make a home for me and for you!

Now, Jesus is the Captain of the angel army,
so if you're ever afraid and don't know what to do...
Just ask Jesus and His angels
to send help from Heaven,
for they are ready and able to protect you!

So, how will you know that an angel is near?

You'll feel the love and joy they bring
in the songs that they sing,
or maybe in a word that you hear.

Even when you don't think there is an angel around,
just open the eyes of your heart and see…

Just ask, "Lord, can I hear their sound?"
Just pray, "God send one to me!"

And when you ask God about something,
and it feels like it's taking too long…
Just imagine the angels on their journey
coming to help you from their heavenly home!

So where are all the angels?
They are all around you every day.
You'll feel them in the stars,

the wind,
in peace,
in love,

in the words you speak when you pray.

They are always with us. Yes with you!
Because God loves you, your angels are given,
especially if you are a child…
for the Bible says your angel
always sees the face of God in Heaven!

15

Draw Your Angel!

Did you know that God created YOU specially?

And that you have your very own angel?

You might have many angels helping you during your life, but the Bible says that you have your own SPECIAL guardian angel!

Why not ask Jesus to help you imagine what your own, special angel friend looks like? Draw your angel here or on your own paper.

You can even ask Jesus what your angel's name is!

Endnotes

PAGE 1

The role of angels in the lives of children is depicted in **Matthew 18:10:** *"See that you do not despise one of these little ones, for I say to you that their angels in heaven continually see the face of My Father who is in heaven."* In this book, we've explored the idea that there is a special connection between angels and children. We've imagined that angels appreciate the playfulness of children as much as they honor their task to protect them.

PAGES 2-3

The Bible reminds us of a strong link between the world of nature that we can see and the world of the angels. Wind and Fire are both mentioned in **Psalm 104:4:** *"He makes the winds His messengers (angels), Flaming fire His ministers."* There is also a scriptural relationship between the stars and angels. Every ancient culture (including the Hebrews) did not see the stars and planets as inanimate, distant objects. They saw them as living, spiritual beings. They are described as having a spiritual voice in **Psalm 19:1-2 (NIV):** *"The heavens declare the glory of God; the skies proclaim the work of his hands. Day after day they pour forth speech; night after night they reveal knowledge."* Then, in **Job 38:4-7 (NIV):** *"Where were you when I laid the earth's foundation? Tell me, if you understand. Who marked off its dimensions? Surely you know! Who stretched a measuring line across it? On what were its footings set, or who laid its cornerstone— while the morning stars sang together and all the angels shouted for joy?"* In **Revelation 12**, we read about stars being swept to the earth by a great dragon. Stars are used here again to describe angels. In this case, it is the angels that were "swept away" by the Devil.

PAGE 4

There is a longstanding Christian tradition of calling some angels "Virtues." They have been a class of angels in historical angel hierarchies, and the title "Virtue," is probably derived from the words for power or stronghold. Here are some scriptures that talk of spiritual, heavenly powers: **Daniel 4:35, Colossians 1:16, Romans 8:38**. There are so many stories of humans seeing angels in a physical form or in a vision. There are too many in the Bible to mention here, but it's clear that seeing and interacting with angels is possible according to the scriptures.

PAGE 5

The first reference is from **Revelation 19:17:** *"Then I saw an angel standing in the sun, and he cried out with a loud voice, saying to all the birds which fly in midheaven, "Come, assemble for the great supper of God."* The angel holding a key is found in **Revelation 20:1-2:** *"Then I saw an angel coming down from heaven, holding the key of the abyss and a great chain in his hand. And he laid hold of the dragon, the serpent of old, who is the devil and Satan, and bound him for a thousand years."* The idea of angels protecting children can be inferred in **Matthew 18:10:** *"See that you do not despise one of these little ones, for I say to you that their angels in heaven continually see the face of My Father who is in heaven."*

PAGE 6

When Daniel first meets Gabriel in the book of **Daniel**, it's in a vision on the banks of a river. From between the banks of the river a voice calls out and sends Gabriel to help Daniel. It's the first mention of an angel's proper name, so it's a big moment in the Biblical timeline. Again, in **chapter 10** of his book, Daniel sees another angel (possibly Gabriel again) while he's by the water. We allowed these connections between Daniel, Gabriel, and water to influence how we imagined this scene. Daniel's angel encounters can be found in **Daniel, chapters 8, 9, and 10**. An angel at the gate to the Garden of Eden can be found in **Genesis 3:24:** *"and at the east of the garden of Eden He stationed the cherubim and the flaming sword which turned every direction to guard the way to the tree of life."*

PAGE 7

There is a well-established tradition of St. Patrick meeting with angels. One of them was called Victoricus (Victor for short). Their close friendship is recorded in *"The Life of Patrick."* (*Celtic Spirituality*, Paulist Press, New York)

Endnotes

PAGE 8

The word "planet" just means "wanderer." The stars that moved through the sky were called the wandering stars by ancient astronomers. Using the same connections between stars and angels mentioned earlier, we wanted to imagine the planets as being connected to the angelic world as well, since they are just stars that move. We also pictured the earth under our feet as part of how the angels are connected to our world. In the **Gospel of Luke**, the stones on the ground are given the same kind of spiritual voice that we saw with the stars. Some of the Pharisees in the crowd said to Him, *"Teacher, rebuke Your disciples." But Jesus answered, "I tell you, if these become silent, the stones will cry out!"* **Luke 19: 39-40.**

PAGE 9

Luke 24: 2-6: *"And they found the stone rolled away from the tomb, but when they entered, they did not find the body of the Lord Jesus. While they were perplexed about this, behold, two men suddenly stood near them in dazzling clothing; and as the women were terrified and bowed their faces to the ground, the men said to them, "Why do you seek the living One among the dead? "He is not here, but He has risen."* **Acts 1: 9-11** *"And after He had said these things, He was lifted up while they were looking on, and a cloud received Him out of their sight. And as they were gazing intently into the sky while He was going, behold, two men in white clothing stood beside them. They also said, "Men of Galilee, why do you stand looking into the sky? This Jesus, who has been taken up from you into heaven, will come in just the same way as you have watched Him go into heaven."*

PAGE 10

We get the ideas of Jesus commanding the heavenly host in a few ways: the first and most direct one is here in **Matthew 26:53:** *"Or do you think that I cannot appeal to My Father, and He will at once put at My disposal more than twelve legions of angels?"* The second comes from a verse in **Joshua 5:14**. There, the "captain of the host of the Lord" appears to Joshua. Some view this as Jesus appearing to him, while others hold that this is an angel too, but one that happens to be in command. Lastly, we have **Ephesians 19-21,** where we see that Jesus Christ has been placed above every spiritual authority. *"These are in accordance with the working of the strength of His might which He brought about in Christ, when He raised Him from the dead and seated Him at His right hand in the heavenly places, far above all rule and authority and power and dominion, and every name that is named, not only in this age but also in the one to come."* And again in **Philippians 2:9-10:** *"For this reason also, God highly exalted Him, and bestowed on Him the name which is above every name, so that at the name of Jesus EVERY KNEE WILL BOW, of those who are in heaven and on earth and under the earth."*

PAGE 11

One easy way to know that the angels are holy, good, and sent from God, is to make sure their presence reflects the character of God. An easy list of traits to remember can be found in **Galatians 5:22-23:** *"But the fruit of the Spirit is love, joy, peace, patience, kindness, goodness, faithfulness, gentleness, self-control; against such things there is no law."* There are two great scripture passages that highlight our God given ability to see things that are unseen. **Ephesians 1:18:** *"I pray that the eyes of your heart may be enlightened, so that you will know what is the hope of His calling, what are the riches of the glory of His inheritance in the saints."* **2 Corinthians 4:17-18:** *"For momentary, light affliction is producing for us an eternal weight of glory far beyond all comparison, while we look not at the things which are seen, but at the things which are not seen; for the things which are seen are temporal, but the things which are not seen are eternal."*

PAGE 12

There is a time when Daniel had asked God for help and it took an angel 3 weeks to get the answer back to Daniel. The angel explains in the passage why it took so long, but it's clear the angel was working hard to get there. *"Do not be afraid, Daniel, for from the first day that you set your heart on understanding this and on humbling yourself before your God, your words were heard, and I have come in response to your words. But the prince of the kingdom of Persia was withstanding me for twenty-one days; then behold, Michael, one of the chief princes, came to help me."* **Daniel 10: 12-13.**

PAGES 13-14

Matthew 18:10: *"See that you do not despise one of these little ones, for I say to you that their angels in heaven continually see the face of My Father who is in heaven."*